Search for the Lost Jedi
GAME BOOK

**The galaxy is yours.
Be a part of**

STAR WARS®

EPISODE I

ADVENTURES

**#1 Search for the Lost Jedi
#2 The Bartokk Assassins**

. . . and more to come!

STAR WARS

EPISODE I

ADVENTURES

GAME BOOK

Search for the Lost Jedi

Ryder Windham

SCHOLASTIC INC.

New York Toronto London Auckland Sydney
Mexico City New Delhi Hong Kong

No part of this publication may be reproduced in whole or in part, of stored in a retrieval system or transmitted in any form or by any means, electronic, mechanical, photocopying, recording, or otherwise, without written permission of the publisher. For information regarding permission, write to Scholastic, Inc., Attention: Permissions Department, 555 Broadway, New York, NY 10012.

ISBN 0-439-12984-2

12 11 10 9 8 7 6 5 4 3 2 1   9/9 0 1 2 3 4/0

Printed in the U.S.A.
First Scholastic printing, September 1999

Search for the Lost Jedi
GAME BOOK

YOUR ADVENTURE BEGINS

For the full story behind your adventure, read up to page 27 in your Star Wars Adventures Novel, *Search for the Lost Jedi*. Or begin here.

You are a Jedi. The *Adventure Guide* contains the rules of *Star Wars Adventures*. You must follow these rules at all times.

Searching for Jedi Master Adi Gallia on the planet Esseles, you encounter reprogrammed droids who have seized the sprawling factory complex of Trinkatta Starships. In an effort to kill all life-forms within the starship factory, the droids are fumigating the building, filling it with toxic smoke.

Your goal is to find Adi Gallia in the starship factory and save her from the fumes. You must also deactivate the rebellious droids and learn the identity of those who commissioned construction of fifty droid starfighters.

Choose your identity from your Character Cards. Although all Jedi Knights are talented and allied with the Force, both Vel Ardox and Noro Zak have unique talents. As an amphibian, Vel Ardox is able to breathe underwater. Noro Zak, a Baxthrax, has massive wings that allow him to fly. Talents are listed on each Character Card.

You can take no more than three weapons/devices (a lightsaber, a breather, and a grappling hook) and one vehicle (it must be useful for traveling overland). You can use Power three times on this adventure.

You start this adventure with 1000 Adventure Points for your Adventure Point (AP) total.

May the Force be with you.

YOUR ADVENTURE:

SEARCH FOR THE LOST JEDI

A plan is quickly hatched to penetrate the starship factory. You will remain at the checkpoint to distract the security droids. Meanwhile, your Jedi allies will try to find another way into the factory. By splitting up and searching different areas of the complex, you will all have a better chance of finding Adi Gallia. Checking your com-links, you will try to stay in contact.

Your three allies head off, leaving you alone at the checkpoint.

A low, mechanical whine causes you to turn. Facing the massive door to the factory, you see it has begun to slide up into the high wall. As the door rises, a bridge comes into view. It's a wide bridge with low guardrails. Suddenly, six security droids emerge from the factory and lurch forward onto the bridge. Seeing you, the droids raise their blaster arms.

Choose to evade the security droids, combat the security droids with your lightsaber, or combat the security droids without using your lightsaber. (If you have any question about how this works, please check out the sample confrontations on page 11 of the *Adventure Guide*.)

To evade the security droids: Roll the 10-dice to leap or fly out of sight of the six droids. The number you roll is your roll#. If flight is one of your talents, your roll# + your skill# (located on your Character Card) + 1 is your adventure#. If flight is not one of your talents, your roll# + your stealth# (located on your Character Card) is your adventure#.

If your adventure# is equal to or more than 8, add the difference (the difference equals your adventure# minus 8) to your AP total. Leaping or flying up to the top of the high wall, the droids lose sight of you and retreat to the factory. You may proceed.

If your adventure# is less than 8, subtract the difference (the difference equals 8 minus your adventure#) from your AP total. You stumbled before you could jump or fly out of sight. Proceed to combat the security droids, either with or without your lightsaber (below).

To combat the security droids with your lightsaber: Roll the 20-dice to use your lightsaber against the droids. The number you roll is your roll#. Your roll# + your weaponry# (located on your Character Card) + your lightsaber's far-range# (located on your Device Card) is your adventure#.

8

If your adventure# is equal to or more than 14, add the difference (the difference equals your adventure# minus 14) to your AP total. Charging forward, you swing fast with your lightsaber, slicing through the security droids before they can fire their blasters. You've destroyed all six droids. You may proceed.

If your adventure# is less than 14, subtract the difference (the difference equals 14 minus your adventure#) from your AP total. The droids fire their blasters before you can get to them. One of the droids nearly shoots you! Roll the 20-dice again. The number you roll is your new roll#. Your new roll# + your weaponry# + 1 is your new adventure#.

> *If your new adventure# is equal to or more than 12,* add 2 AP to your AP total. You neatly sever the six droids' heads from their shoulders. They collapse upon the bridge. You may proceed.

> *If your new adventure# is less than 12,* subtract the difference from your AP total. You can't get into close enough range to effectively use your lightsaber. Proceed to combat the security droids without using your lightsaber (next page).

To combat the security droids without using your lightsaber: Roll the 20-dice to lure the six droids across the bridge and under the sliding door. The number you roll is your roll#. Your roll# + your skill# (located on your Character Card) + your stealth# (also located on your Character Card) is your adventure#.

If your adventure# is equal to or more than 14, add the difference (the difference equals your adventure# minus 14) to your AP total. Stepping into the security checkpoint booth, you flip a switch to lower the massive door. As the six droids run to catch you, they are crushed under the descending door. You flip the switch to raise the door . . . and find that it's jammed! You must unjam the door (below).

If your adventure# is less than 14, subtract the difference (the difference equals 14 minus your adventure#) from your AP total. Go back to the line *To combat the security droids without using your lightsaber* and try again.

To unjam the door: Roll the 20-dice to open the massive door. If repair is one of your talents, your roll# + your skill# (located on your Character Card) + 2 is your adventure#. If repair is not one of your talents, your roll# + your strength# (located on your Character Card) + 1 is your adventure#.

If your adventure# is equal to or more than 11, add 3 AP to your AP total. The door rises and you may proceed.

If your adventure# is less than 11, subtract 3 AP from your AP total. Go back to the line *To unjam the door* and try again.

Moving away from the sliding door, you begin to cross the bridge toward the starship factory. The bridge is suspended ten meters over a deep, water-filled moat.

You wonder if your battle with the security droids has allowed your friends time to find another way into the starship factory. You decide to try contacting the other Jedi. Switching on your comlink, you whisper, "I'm on the bridge that leads to the entrance! Are you inside the factory yet?"

"Not yet!" answers one Jedi. "We ran into some more droids. Getting in will be more difficult than we realized."

Switching off your comlink, you begin to cross the bridge toward the factory entrance. Halfway across, a bright glint from above catches your attention.

Three stories up, on a rooftop that supports an elevated water tower, you see eight security droids running into position. Suddenly, the menacing droids raise their blaster rifles, preparing to fire from above.

You doubt you can defeat the droids one at a time, but you might be able to wipe all of them out if you can destroy the water tower. To save yourself, choose to destroy the water tower or hide under the guard rail.

To destroy the water tower: Roll the 20-dice to use your lightsaber. If defense is one of your talents, your roll# + your weaponry# + your lightsaber's far-range# + 1 is your adventure#. If defense is not one of your talents, your roll# + your weaponry# + your lightsaber's far-range# is your adventure#.

If your adventure# is equal to or more than 12, add the difference to your AP total. The droids fire their blaster rifles. Swinging fast with your lightsaber, you strike the oncoming energy bolts, batting them at the elevated water tower above the droids. Your aim is perfect. The water tower explodes, knocking down the droids. The devastating cascade reaches the bridge, sweeping your from your hiding place and into the moat! You may proceed!

If your adventure# is less than 12, subtract 5 AP from your AP total. Striking at the fired energy bolts, you try batting them at the water tower . . . but miss. Roll the 20-dice again. Your new roll# + your weaponry# + your lightsaber's far-range# + 2 is your new adventure#.

If your new adventure# is equal to or more than 13, add 2 AP to your AP total. Deflecting the energy bolts back at the water tower, you create a flood that knocks down the droids. The pressure of the watery blast flushes you off the bridge and into the moat. You may proceed.

If your new adventure# is less than 13, subtract the difference from your AP total. You're lucky you weren't vaporized! Proceed to hide under the guardrail (below).

To hide under the guardrail: Roll the 10-dice to duck under the bridge's guardrail, using it as protective cover from the droids' blaster fire. Your roll# + your stealth# is your adventure#.

If your adventure# is equal to or more than 6, add the difference to your AP total. Hiding under the guardrail, you hear the droids' energy bolts striking above and around you. Although you're protected from being hit, you realize your only way out is down into the moat. You dive down and proceed.

If your adventure# is less than 6, subtract 1 AP from your AP total. You throw yourself under the rail so hard that you fall past it, straight into the moat. You may proceed.

You plunge into the cool depths of the icy moat. More droids continue the attack, firing energy bolts into the water and nearly hitting you. Hoping to get out of the droids' firing range, you swim directly beneath the bridge to the underwater foundation of the starship factory.

Adjusting your vision in the murky depths, you see what appears to be the opening of an underwater tunnel in the building's foundation. You hope it's an entrance to the factory and decide to enter the dark hole.

To swim through the underwater tunnel, choose to hold your breath or use your breather.

To hold your breath: Roll the 10-dice to swim through the tunnel. If breathing underwater is one of your talents, your roll# + your skill# + 3 is your adventure#. If breathing under-water is not one of your abilities, your roll# + your strength# is your adventure#.

If your adventure# is equal to or more than 7, add the difference to your AP total. Rising to the surface, you take a deep breath, then re-turn to the underwater tunnel. You may pro-ceed.

If your adventure# is less than 7, subtract the difference from your AP total. You rise to the surface to take one last breath of air, but the polluted air surrounding the factory makes you cough. Proceed to use your breather (be-low).

To use your breather: Roll the 20-dice to wear your breather for your underwater journey. Your roll# + your strength# + your breather's far-range# is your adventure#.

If your adventure# is equal to or more than 13, add the difference to your AP total. By swimming into the tunnel, you have gained entry into the starship factory. You may pro-ceed.

If your adventure# is less than 13, subtract the difference from your AP total. You acciden-

tally inhaled some water. Go back to the line
To use your breather and try again.

You propel yourself forward through the water-filled tunnel. Seconds later, you are engulfed by pitch-black darkness. You concentrate on the interior of the cave, using the Force to sense the barely visible walls. Absent of fear, you swim forward.

For surviving your encounter with the security droids and gaining access to the starship factory, add 100 AP to your AP total.

Soon, the tunnel narrows, making it difficult to swim. Reaching out with your hands and feet, you can just manage a crawl through the underwater access. You feel along the walls of the tunnel, trying to find your grip, but the stone is covered with an oily muck.

Suddenly, something slimy bumps against your leg. In the next instant, your left ankle is caught in a tight grip.

You're not alone!

You reach to your lower leg — and touch

a thick tentacle coiled around your foot! Snaking out from a hole in the tunnel wall, the tentacle tugs your ankle, drawing you into the gap. Some broken stones from the foundation lie below the hole.

It is possible the unseen creature is merely defending its territory. There is also the possibility the creature wants you for its next meal. If you can communicate with the creature, you might avoid any misunderstanding.

Choose to communicate with the creature (using Power), escape, or fight the creature.

To communicate with the creature (using Power): Choose your Persuasion Power. Roll the 10-dice to send a mental message to the tentacled creature, conveying you mean no harm. Your roll# + your Power# + your Power's mid-resist# is your adventure#.

If your adventure# is equal to or more than 9, add the difference to your AP total. The sensitive creature releases you immediately, admitting that it was scared by your presence in the tunnel. The creature apologizes for its attack and wishes you well on your mission. You may proceed.

If your adventure# is less than 9, subtract 4 AP from your AP total. The primitive creature is a mindless carnivore, intent only on devouring you. Proceed to escape or fight the creature (below).

*NOTE: This counts as one of the three Power uses you are allowed on this adventure.

To escape the creature: Roll the 10-dice to pull your leg free of the creature's grip. Your roll# + your strength# + 2 is your adventure#.

If your adventure# is equal to or more than 9, add the difference to your AP total. Kicking sharply, your foot slips out of the tentacle. You leave the creature behind, and may proceed.

If your adventure# is less than 9, subtract the difference from your AP total. Unable to pull your leg free from the coils of the tentacle, you must proceed to fight the creature (below).

To fight the creature: Roll the 10-dice to pick up a foundation stone from the tunnel floor and drop it on the creature's tentacle. Your roll# + your strength# is your adventure#.

If your adventure# is equal to or more than 7, add the difference to your AP total. Smashing the creature's tentacle, you are released from its grip. In a rush of bubbles, the tentacle vanishes into the hole in the foundation and you may proceed.

If your adventure# is less than 7, subtract the difference from your AP total. You barely bruised the creature's tentacle. Roll the 10-dice again to smash the stone between the tentacle and the gap in the foundation. Your new roll# + your strength# + 1 is your new adventure#.

> *If your new adventure# is equal to or more than 8,* add 2 AP to your AP total. The stone pins the creature's tentacle within the gap. The startled creature releases its grip and you may proceed.

> *If your new adventure# is less than 8,* subtract the difference from your AP total and repeat this confrontation (from the line "Roll the 10-dice again to smash the stone between the tentacle and the gap in the foundation") until you have jammed the stone into the foundation. Once you have pinned the creature, you may proceed.

Leaving the creature behind, you swim on through the underwater tunnel. A steady, mechanical thumping sound grows louder as you move forward. When you try to listen to the sound, you realize you're still moving through the tunnel. Caught in a powerful current, you're being dragged deeper into the darkness.

The mechanical thumping sound becomes increasingly louder. Battling the current, you extend your arms and legs, trying to brace yourself within the tunnel. The walls are coated with a mucky substance and you are unable to grab anything. You feel as if you're being flushed through a greased tube.

Unable to stop your rapid journey, you're dragged onward by the current. The suction becomes stronger — you must blindly struggle to keep your body from bouncing off the walls. As the water pressure becomes almost unbearable, you see what appears to be a blurry, glowing circle in the distance. The circle becomes larger and brighter, and you realize you're approaching the illuminated end of the tunnel.

You don't know what possible dangers await you in the beyond. In a last, desperate attempt to slow your course, you smash your hands against the walls. Mud squishes between your knuckles as you're swept on by the unrelenting torrent.

In an explosive surge, a concentrated waterfall forces you out of the tunnel. Wildly disoriented, you plummet through the air and showering water. You angle your head to see that you're falling toward a pool at the base of a wide, circular silo. An instant later, you splash down into the pool. You must arc your body to lift your head above the surface.

The thumping sound is now nearly deafening, echoing off the silo walls in thunderous booms. Like a gigantic drain, the water churns and swirls around you, dragging you below the surface. Suddenly you realize what's making the horrendous noise.

At the base of the silo, a giant propeller spins rapidly, drawing the water down. Built to circulate water in the factory's moat, the great hydraulic propeller will slice you to bits unless you escape the silo.

You struggle against the downward flow and break the surface of the pool. Pounded by water falling from above, you swim for the silo wall. The inner silo appears to be lined with a thick layer of ferrocrete, a mixture of concrete and steel-like materials bonded at the molecular level. Like the tunnel, the silo wall is too slick for a handhold.

You look up to the top of the silo, and see a maintenance hatch. The hatch is illuminated by several greenish-yellow glow rods dangling from a narrow beam.

Choose to disable the giant propeller or to escape to the upper hatch. You may try to disable the giant propeller with or without Power. If flight is one of your talents, you can fly to the hatch. Otherwise, you must throw your grappling hook.

To disable the giant propeller (using Power)': Choose your Alteration Power. Roll the 10-dice to use Power to bend the propeller blades. Your roll# + your Power# + your Power's mid-resist# + 1 is your adventure#.

If your adventure# is equal to or more than 10, add the difference to your AP total. The propeller blades bend and snag against the drainage walls, jamming the system. The pump shuts down, but water continues to pour into the silo. Because of the slowed drain, the water level rises within the silo, carrying you to the upper hatch. You may proceed.

If your adventure# is less than 10, subtract the difference from your AP total. Your concentration was weak; you must focus your mind on bending the propeller blades. Roll the 10-dice again. Your new roll# + your Power# + your Power's mid-resist# is your new adventure#.

> *If your new adventure# is equal to or more than 10,* add 3 AP to your AP total. Destroying the propeller, you slow the drain and rise to the upper hatch. You may proceed.

> *If your new adventure# is less than 10,* subtract the difference from your AP total. Proceed to escape to the upper hatch, either by flying (next page) or by throwing your grappling hook (page 25).

*NOTE: This counts as one of three Power uses you are allowed on this adventure.

To disable the giant propeller (without Power): Roll the 20-dice to cut a chunk out of the silo wall with your lightsaber. Your roll# + your weaponry# + your weapon's close-range# + 2 is your adventure#.

If your adventure# is equal to or more than 16, add the difference to your AP total. Treading water, you hold your lightsaber high over your head and activate the blade. You swing at the silo wall, carving out a large chunk of ferrocrete. You deactivate your lightsaber as the heavy chunk breaks away from the wall and splashes into the water. The debris sinks to the bottom of the silo where it smashes the propeller blades. The pump shuts down, but water continues to pour into the silo. Because of the slowed drain, the water level rises within the silo, carrying you to the upper hatch. You may proceed.

If your adventure# is less than 16, subtract 5 AP from your AP total. Treading water, you swing your lightsaber and cut a large chunk of ferrocrete from the wall. The chunk sinks to the bottom of the silo but barely dents the massive propeller. If flight is one of your talents, proceed to fly up to the hatch (below). If flight is not one of your talents, proceed to throw your grappling hook (next page).

To fly up to the hatch: Flight *must* be one of your talents. Roll the 10-dice to soar up through the silo and land on a ledge in front of the hatch. Your roll# + your skill# + 2 is your adventure#.

If your adventure# is equal to or more than 8, add the difference to your AP total. Soaring up from the pool to the top of the silo, you land on the ledge and examine the hatch. You may proceed.

If your adventure# is less than 8, subtract the difference from your AP total. The falling water drives you back into the pool. Proceed to throw your grappling hook (below).

To throw your grappling hook: Roll the 20-dice to hurl your grappling hook to the glow rods hanging from the distant ceiling. Your grappling hook is tied to a thin cable that will allow you to climb to the hatch. Your roll# + your strength# + your grappling hook's far-range# is your adventure#.

If your adventure# is equal to or more than 14, add the difference to your AP total. Snagging the glow rods with your grappling hook, you tug at the cable. With a secure line, proceed to climb the cable (below).

If your adventure# is less than 14, subtract 7 AP from your AP total. You'll have to throw harder than that. Roll the 20-dice again. Your new roll# + your strength# + your grappling hook's far-range# is your new adventure#.

If your new adventure# is equal to or more than 13, add 2 AP to your AP total. You snag the glow rods with your grappling hook, then tug at the cable. The line is secure. Proceed to climb the cable (below).

If your new adventure# is less than 13, subtract the difference from your AP total and repeat (from the line "Roll the 20-dice again") until you have thrown your grappling hook to the glow rods. When you have snagged the glow rods with the hook, proceed to climb the cable (below).

To climb the cable: Roll the 10-dice to climb to the upper hatch. Your grappling hook is tied to a thin cable that will allow you to climb to the hatch. Your roll# + your strength# + 1 is your adventure#.

If your adventure# is equal to or more than 8, add the difference to your AP total. Hand over hand, you scramble up the cable faster than a Kowakian monkey-lizard. You may proceed.

If your adventure# is less than 8, subtract the difference from your AP total. Your weight causes the glow rod to pull out of the ceiling, prompting you to fall back down into the water. Looking up at the other glow rods, you find one that appears to be more secure. You must try snagging another glow rod. Go back to the line *To throw your grappling hook* and try again.

Perching on a narrow ledge in front of the metal maintenance hatch, you check your gear.

For escaping death in the water passageways beneath the starship factory, add 75 AP to your AP total.

If you wore your breather, you have depleted its air supply. Until you can refill the breather, you cannot use it again on this adventure. If you have not yet worn your breather, you do not need to refill it. Fortunately, toxic fumes have not reached the interior of the silo.

Your lightsaber is fine, but the water has ruined your comlink. Without the comlink, you can't communicate with the other Jedi. You must proceed on your own.

An old wheel-shaped opening mechanism is affixed to the hatch. If you are to break into the starship factory, you must get through this hatchway. Gripping the wheel, you prepare to give it a hard turn.

To turn the wheel on the hatch: Roll the 10-dice to open the hatch. Your roll# + your strength# is your adventure#.

If your adventure# is equal to or more than 7, add 25 AP to your AP total. The wheel turns easily and the hatch opens. Entering the hatch, you escape the silo and may proceed.

If your adventure# is less than 7, subtract the difference from your AP total. You turn the wheel . . . and it snaps off in your hands! You toss the useless old thing aside, letting it fall to the churning water below. To open the hatch, choose to use Power on the hatch's lock, cut open the hatch with your lightsaber, or kick the hatch in (next page).

To open the hatch's lock (using Power)*: Choose your Alteration Power. Roll the 10-dice to unlock the hatch by using the Force. Your roll# + your Power# + your Power's low-resist# is your adventure#.

If your adventure# is equal to or more than 9, add the difference to your AP total. Focusing on the lock, you use the Force to slide the bolt and unlock the hatch. Pushing open the hatch, you may proceed.

If your adventure# is less than 9, subtract the difference from your AP total. When you swam through the underwater tunnel, you forgot to turn off your lightsaber's power. The lightsaber is fried and must recharge. Proceed to kick the hatch in (below).

*NOTE: This counts as one of three Power uses you are allowed on this adventure.

To kick the hatch in: Roll the 10-dice to launch a kick at the rusted hatch. Your roll# + your strength# + 1 is your adventure#.

If your adventure# is equal to or more than 7, add the difference to your AP total. With a single kick, the hatch crashes inward, allowing you to escape the silo. You may proceed.

If your adventure# is less than 7, subtract the difference from your AP total. Although heavily rusted, the hatch's metal is still quite strong and you hurt your foot. Still, you managed to loosen the hatch. Roll the 10-dice again to throw all your weight against it. Your new roll# + your strength# + 2 is your new adventure#.

If your new adventure# is equal to or more than 7, add 2 AP to your AP total. The hatch is demolished and you may proceed.

If your new adventure# is less than 7, subtract the difference from your AP total and repeat from the phrase "Roll the 10-dice again" until you have opened the hatch. Then you may proceed.

Passing through the hatchway, you enter a large subterranean chamber. Dimly illuminated by glow rods, the stone-walled room smells of dust and decay. In the center of the chamber, three tall pillars rise from the stone floor to the brick ceiling.

"Unnnnn," a voice moans from behind one pillar. Running around the column, you find a semiconscious alien lying on the floor. He is a small yellow-scaled reptilian creature with a pronounced beak, clothed in a fine tunic. His right arm is missing below the elbow joint and his left foot is chained to the pillar.

"Are you okay?" you ask the alien as you check his pulse.

"Oh, I'm just fine," the alien groans, "except that the droids cut off my arm and locked me up here to die."

Your eyes go wide. "The droids cut off your arm?!"

"They were trying to get information out of me," the alien sighs. "No big deal. I'm a

Kloodavian. The arm'll grow back in a couple of days."

"What are you doing in here?" you ask.

"I should be asking *you* that question!" the Kloodavian snarls. "I'm Boll Trinkatta! I *own* this starship factory! But my droids went berserk and took over. I don't know how, but someone must've reprogrammed them! The droids brought me down here and left me to die."

Before you can ask any more questions of Boll Trinkatta, an eight-armed maintenance droid rolls out from behind one of the other pillars. Hiding out of view, it has waited for this moment to attack. Each of its eight arms wields a different tool, including a beamdrill, fusioncutter, macrofuser, and power prybar. Extending its appendages, the droid accelerates, heading straight for you.

Choose to dodge or combat the droid. If you choose combat, decide whether to use your lightsaber or Power.

To dodge the droid: Roll the 20-dice to leap away from the oncoming maintenance droid. If defense is one of your talents, your roll# + your

stealth# + your strength# + 2 is your adventure#.
If defense is not one of your talents, your roll# +
your stealth# + your strength# is your adventure#.

*If your adventure# is equal to or more than
14,* add the difference to your AP total. You
leap aside as the maintenance droid races forward. Unable to stop in time, the droid
crashes into the wall. The droid is ruined and
you may proceed.

If your adventure# is less than 14, subtract the
difference from your AP total. The maintenance droid chases you. Proceed to combat
the droid by using your lightsaber (below).

**To combat the droid (using a
lightsaber):** Roll the 10-dice to cut down the
eight-armed maintenance droid. Your roll# +
your weaponry# + your lightsaber's close-range#
is your adventure#.

If your adventure# is equal to or more than 8,
add the difference to your AP total. Activating
the lightsaber, you swing at the droid, cleaving
it at the head and arm sockets. The maintenance droid is destroyed and you may proceed.

If your adventure# is less than 8, subtract the
difference from your AP total. Your lightsaber

sputters, prompting you to reactivate it. Roll the 10-dice again. Your new roll# + your weaponry# + your lightsaber's close-range# + 1 is your new adventure#.

If your new adventure# is equal to or more than 10, add 2 AP to your AP total. With your lightsaber blazing, you duck and turn, slicing through the maintenance droid and lopping its head off. The droid is destroyed and you may proceed.

If your new adventure# is less than 10, subtract the difference from your AP total. Your lightsaber's power unit requires more charging. Proceed to combat the droid by using Power (below).

To combat the droid (using Power)*:
Choose your Alteration Power. Roll the 20-dice. Your roll# + your Power# + your Power's mid-resist# + your skill# is your adventure#.

If your adventure# is equal to or more than 14, add the difference to your AP total. The droid drills and claws at its own torso, ripping out its processing unit with a manipulator claw. Unable to function without its processing unit, the droid is reduced to scrap. You may proceed.

If your adventure# is less than 14, subtract the difference from your AP total and repeat until you have made the maintenance droid attack itself. When the droid is ruined, you may proceed.

*NOTE: This counts as one of three Power uses you are allowed on this adventure.

Stepping away from the remains of the fallen droid, you approach Trinkatta, still leaning against the pillar. With surprise in his eyes, the Kloodavian remarks, "Only a Jedi moves that fast!"

Ignoring Trinkatta's comment, you look him in the eyes. "A woman came here to inspect your building," you say, maintaining secrecy by not mentioning Adi Gallia's name. "You will tell me where I can find her."

Trinkatta glares at you but doesn't answer.

"You're in a lot of trouble, friend. I know you're selling fifty droid starfighters. I want to know the identity of the buyer. Direct me to your factory's central droid control room."

"I . . . I don't have to tell you anything!" Trinkatta insists.

You are uncertain whether the Kloodavian is arrogant or afraid to answer your questions. To make Trinkatta answer your questions, choose to tell the truth, use the Force (using Power), or frighten the Kloodavian.

To tell the truth: Roll the 10-dice to make an honest appeal to the alien, telling him that you are a Jedi on a secret mission, trying to save someone who is important to both you and the galaxy. Your roll# + your charm# + 2 is your adventure#.

If your adventure# is equal to or more than 9, add 7 AP to your AP total. Boll Trinkatta is impressed that you are a Jedi. He promises to answer all your questions. He only asks for your help to unchain him. You may proceed.

If your adventure# is less than 9, subtract 7 AP from your AP total. Boll Trinkatta looks at you with a bored expression. Either he doesn't believe you're a Jedi or he just doesn't care. Proceed to use the Force, or frighten the Kloodavian (next page).

To use the Force (using Power):* You must be a Jedi in order to do this. Roll the 10-dice to use the Force, making the Kloodavian tell you everything you want to know. Your roll# + your Power# + 2 is your adventure#.

If your adventure# is equal to or more than 8, add the difference to your AP total. Boll Trinkatta politely informs you that Kloodavians are immune to Jedi mind tricks. However, Trinkatta says he'll be happy to answer your questions if you'll release him from his shackles. Agreeing to release him, you may proceed.

If your adventure# is less than 8, subtract the difference from your AP total. Boll Trinkatta laughs in your face, informing you that Jedi mind tricks don't work on Kloodavians. "I don't have to tell you anything!" he sneers. To make him answer your questions, proceed to frighten the Kloodavian (below).

***NOTE:** This counts as one of three Power uses you are allowed on this adventure.

To frighten the Kloodavian: Roll the 10-dice to bluff. You tell Boll Trinkatta you'll inform his rebellious droids that he is responsible for ruining the eight-armed maintenance droid (the one *you* destroyed) and is going to go after

36

them next. Your roll# + your charm# is your adventure#.

If your adventure# is equal to or more than 7, add the difference to your AP total. Afraid the other droids will believe you and punish him even more, Trinkatta will answer your questions. You may proceed.

If your adventure# is less than 7, subtract the difference from your AP total. Sputtering with laughter, Trinkatta calls your bluff. The little Kloodavian doesn't scare easily. Roll the 10-dice again. Your new roll# + your skill# + 1 is your new adventure#.

> *If your new adventure# is equal to or more than 9,* add 2 AP to your AP total. Something in your piercing gaze makes Trinkatta think you might not be bluffing after all. Fearing the droids will come back to attack him, Trinkatta answers your questions. You may proceed.

> *If your new adventure# is less than 9,* subtract the difference from your AP total and repeat this confrontation from the line "Roll the 10-dice again" until the Kloodavian answers your questions. Then you may proceed.

You set to work on the lock, careful not to injure the Kloodavian's leg. "I don't know anything about a building inspector," Trinkatta confides. "It's possible she was captured by my droids after they'd already locked me up."

"What about the location of your central droid control room?" you ask.

"It's on Level 19 of the observation tower, on the other side of the factory's spaceport," Trinkatta replies.

Working a thin wire into the manacle at Trinkatta's foot, you inquire, "And who ordered the fifty droid starfighters?"

Trinkatta gulps, nervous to answer this final question. "I . . . I built them for the Trade Federation."

"The Trade Federation?!" you exclaim. "That doesn't make any sense! This planet isn't anywhere near Trade Federation routes. Why did they commission *you* to build fifty droid starfighters?"

"I don't know why they picked me," Trinkatta admitted. "Every starship maker in the galaxy knows the Xi Charrians have an exclusive contract to build droid starfighters for the Trade Federation.

When the Neimoidians told me they wanted me to install hyperdrive engines into the fighters, I protested. The next day, my test pilot vanished! I was afraid if I didn't follow the Trade Federation's orders, they'd make me disappear too."

"Where are the droid starfighters now?" you ask.

"I wish I knew!" Trinkatta squawks. "That's what my own malfunctioning droids kept asking me when they locked me up. Someone stole all fifty starfighters. When the Neimoidians find out, they'll kill me!"

"We'll worry about the Trade Federation later," you remark as you unchain Trinkatta from the pillar. "Your droids closed off the factory's chimneys and the whole complex is filling up with fumes. If my friend is in the building, she'll die unless I can rescue her!"

"I'd offer to help," Trinkatta moans, "but I'm no good to you with this busted arm of mine." Aiming his beak toward a narrow hallway, he says, "That hall leads to the starship assembly room. You can open the chimneys from the assembly operations chamber. From there, you'll have to cross the spaceport to the observation tower. I hope you find your friend."

"You can't stay here!" you shout. "If the fumes reach you . . ."

"I can take care of myself!" the Kloodavian retorts. "I have a secret tunnel that leads outside the factory. You'd better go while you can!"

Leaving Trinkatta behind, you run down the hallway. Hearing your approach, two factory operations droids step out at the end of the hall, blocking your entrance to the starship assembly room. Both droids have broad upper bodies supported on strong but narrow legs. They stare at you through late-model photoreceptors, the kind that easily fry when suddenly exposed to bright light.

Choose to blind, dodge, or combat the factory operations droids. If you choose combat, choose to combat both droids at once or one at a time.

To blind the factory operations droids: Roll the 10-dice to activate your lightsaber. Your roll# + your weaponry# + your weapon's mid-range# is your adventure#.

If your adventure# is equal to or more than 9, add the difference to your AP total. The sudden flash of your lightsaber fries the optic circuits within the droids' photoreceptors. As the droids stumble into each other, you walk past them. You may proceed.

If your adventure# is less than 9, subtract the difference from your AP total. The droids lower their protective visors before your lightsaber's glare can fry their photoreceptors. Proceed to dodge the factory operations droids (below) or combat them (next page).

To dodge the factory operations droids: Roll the 10-dice to get past the droids. If flight is one of your abilities, your roll# + your skill# + your stealth# is your adventure#. If flight is not one of your abilities, your roll# + your stealth# is your adventure#.

If your adventure# is equal to or more than 8, add the difference to your AP total. If flight is one of your abilities, you soar over the heads of the two droids and into the starship assembly room. If flight is not one of your abilities, you dive through the narrow space between the two droids. Turning fast to pursue you, the two operations droids stumble over one another's feet and crash to the floor. You may proceed.

41

If your adventure# is less than 8, subtract the difference from your AP total. You stumble in the hall. Proceed to combat both droids at once (below):

To combat both droids at once: Roll the 20-dice to lasso the factory operations droids' ankles with your grappling hook. Your roll# + your strength# + your grappling hook's mid-range# is your adventure#.

If your adventure# is equal to or more than 13, add the difference to your AP total. Catching both droids with your grappling hook, you pull hard on the cable. The operations droids clatter to the floor and you may proceed.

If your adventure# is less than 13, subtract the difference from your AP total. Both droids dodge the grappling hook and reach for their fusioncutters. Proceed to combat one droid at a time (below).

To combat one droid at a time: Roll the 10-dice to use your lightsaber against the droids. Your roll# + your weaponry# + your lightsaber's mid-range# + 1 is your adventure#.

If your adventure# is equal to or more than 10, add the difference to your AP total. Using the same adventure#, repeat this confrontation from the beginning to destroy the second droid. After both factory operations droids are cut down, you may proceed.

If your adventure# is less than 10, subtract the difference from your AP total. Firing its fusioncutter, the droid nearly fries you. Roll the 10-dice again. Your new roll# + your weaponry# + your lightsaber's mid-range# + 2 is your new adventure#.

> *If your new adventure# is equal to or more than 10*, add 3 AP to your AP total. Your lightsaber slices the droid in half. If necessary, repeat this confrontation to destroy the second droid. When both droids lie in pieces on the starship assembly floor, you may proceed.

> *If your new adventure# is less than 10*, subtract the difference from your AP total and repeat this confrontation from the line "Roll the 10-dice again" until you have struck down both operations droids. Then you may proceed.

Entering the starship assembly room, you find it filled with a haze of smoke. Looking nine stories up to the ceiling, you can barely see the windows that line the higher levels. Across the room, beyond several rows of starships and repulsorlift vehicles at various stages of construction, you see the assembly operations chamber. According to Trinkatta, the controls for the factory's chimneys are in the operations chamber, but you're uncertain of how long you can survive in the smoke-filled room. Coughing, you spot an air compressor unit.

Choose to use your breather or hold your breath. If your breather's air supply is depleted, you must first refill the breather before wearing it.

To refill your breather's air supply (if necessary): Roll the 10-dice to fill your breather from the air compressor unit. Your roll# + your skill# is your adventure#.

If your adventure# is equal to or more than 6, add the difference to your AP total. In seconds, your breather is fully charged with air. To reach the assembly operations chamber, proceed to use your breather (next page).

If your adventure# is less than 6, subtract the difference from your AP total. The air compressor unit is broken. Proceed to fix the air compressor (below) or hold your breath (next page).

To fix the air compressor: Roll the 10-dice to repair the broken compressor unit. If repair is one of your talents, your roll# + your knowledge# + your skill# is your adventure#. If repair is not one of your talents, your roll# + your skill# + 1 is your adventure#.

If your adventure# is equal to or more than 8, add the difference to your AP total. Your nimble fingers repair the air compressor and you quickly refill the charge in your breather. Proceed to use your breather (below).

If your adventure# is less than 8, subtract the difference from your AP total. Unable to fix the broken compressor, you must proceed to hold your breath (next page).

To use your breather: Roll the 20-dice to wear your breather across the smoke-filled room. Your roll# + your skill# + your breather's mid-range# is your adventure#.

If your adventure# is equal to or more than 14, add the difference to your AP total. Wearing your breather, you pass the starship assembly lines to the operations chamber. You may proceed.

If your adventure# is less than 14, subtract 6 AP from your AP total. Tripping over a loose cable, you fall to the floor and accidentally crack your breather. Discarding the broken apparatus, proceed to hold your breath (below).

To hold your breath: Roll the 10-dice to walk through toxic air. Your roll# + your strength# is your adventure#.

If your adventure# is equal to or more than 7, add the difference to your AP total. Taking a deep breath, you run past the partially assembled starships to the operations chamber. The air is breathable there, and you may proceed.

If your adventure# is less than 7, subtract the difference from your AP total. You hold your breath and step forward, but the smoke gets thicker and impairs your vision. Blinking your eyes, you stumble and fall down a steep slide that leads to a junk metal scrapper. As soon as you strike the slide, you automatically activate the scrapper's whirling metal thresher at the bottom of the smooth slide. You must stop your descent down the slide before you're mangled. This time, roll the 20-dice to escape the slide. If flight is one of your talents, your roll# + your stealth# + 5 is your adventure#. If flight is not one of your talents, your new roll#

+ your stealth# + your strength# + 1 is your new adventure#.

If your new adventure# is equal to or more than 11, add 3 AP to your AP total. You fly or jump up and away from the slide, landing near where you stumbled. Keeping low to the floor to avoid the smoke, you scramble past the partially assembled starships to the assembly operations chamber. The air is breathable there, and you may proceed.

If your new adventure# is less than 11, subtract the difference from your AP total. You have slowed your progress — but you're not safe yet. You must repeat this confrontation from the line "This time, roll the 20-dice to escape the slide," until you have escaped the junk metal scrapper and reached the assembly operations chamber. Then you may proceed.

Entering the assembly operations chamber, you find its computer circuits have been ripped apart. The droids must have tried destroying the controls to prevent anyone from opening the chimneys and allowing the smoke to escape.

An unfinished starfighter rests on a nearby conveyer system. The ship isn't ready to fly but its laser cannons appear to be operational. You also notice a repulsor-lift vehicle, usually used to shuttle parts throughout the factory. Although it doesn't have any weapons, the repulsorlift should be able to rise all the way to the factory ceiling.

To stop smoke from filling up the factory, choose to repair the controls and open the chimneys, fire an unfinished starfighter's laser cannons at the ceiling, or launch a repulsorlift vehicle at the factory ceiling.

To repair the controls: Roll the 20-dice to rewire the controls and open the chimneys. If repair is one of your talents, your roll# + your knowledge# + your skill# + 2 is your adventure#. If repair is not one of your talents, your roll# + your knowledge# + your skill# is your adventure#.

If your adventure# is equal to or more than 14, add the difference to your AP total. The droids did a lousy job of trying to destroy the control room. In seconds, you manage to get the controls online and open the factory's three chimneys. The smoke dissipates and you may proceed.

If your adventure# is less than 14, subtract the difference from your AP total. You have accidentally activated the master switch to the assembly room's automated equipment. Suddenly, every piece of machinery roars to life. A warning light flashes on the console, indicating the sudden power surge will cause a horrendous explosion. To deactivate the equipment, you must remain calm. This time, roll the 10-dice to prevent the assembly room from exploding. If calm is one of your talents, your new roll# + your knowledge# + 2 is your new adventure#. If calm is not one of your talents, your new roll# + your knowledge# is your new adventure#.

If your new adventure# is equal to or more than 6, add the difference to your AP total. You deactivate the master switch and turn off all the assembly room's automated machinery. Go back to the line *To repair the controls* and try to open the factory's chimneys again.

If your new adventure# is less than 6, subtract 10 AP from your AP total. The assembly operations computer overheats and shorts out, causing the automated machinery to shut down. Because the computer is totally disabled, you cannot use it to open the factory's chimneys. Proceed to fire an unfinished starfighter's laser cannons at the ceiling (below).

To fire an unfinished starfighter's laser cannons at the ceiling: Roll the 10-dice to activate the vessel's weapon system. Your roll# + your weaponry# + 3 is your adventure#.

If your adventure# is equal to or more than 9, add the difference to your AP total. Climbing into the cockpit of the unfinished starfighter, you adjust the laser cannons and target the ceiling. Firing, you blast through the roof, allowing the backed-up smoke to escape. You may proceed.

If your adventure# is less than 9, subtract the difference from your AP total. The unfinished starfighter's targeting computer was not properly calibrated, and the fired blast strikes a wide girder near the ceiling. The girder buckles, sending a tremor throughout the entire building. One more misfired shot and the entire assembly room could cave in on top of you. Roll the 10-dice again to fix the targeting computer. If repair is one of your talents, your new roll# + your skill# + your knowledge# is your new adventure#. If repair is not one of your talents, your new roll# + your knowledge# is your new adventure#.

If your new adventure# is equal to or more than 7, add the difference to your AP total. After repairing the targeting computer, you fire a blast that knocks a hole through the roof. The smoke rises out of the factory and you may proceed.

If your new adventure# is less than 7, subtract 4 AP from your AP total. The targeting computer is broken. Proceed to launch a repulsorlift vehicle at the factory ceiling (below).

To launch a repulsorlift vehicle at the factory ceiling: Roll the 10-dice to activate the launch mechanism for a nearly completed repulsorlift vehicle that sits on the assembly line. Your roll# + your skill# + 2 is your adventure#.

If your adventure# is equal to or more than 7, add the difference to your AP total. Rigging the repulsorlift's launch mechanism, you aim the vessel for the ceiling and activate the thrusters. Leaping away from the unmanned repulsorlift, you dive for cover as it roars up to the ceiling and smashes a huge hole through the roof. While the smoke rises up through the hole in the roof, the repulsorlift crashes to the ground outside the factory. You may proceed.

If your adventure# is less than 7, subtract the difference from your AP total. The repulsorlift's thrusters stall. Roll the 10-dice again. Your new roll# + your skill# + 3 is your new adventure#.

If your new adventure# is equal to or more than 7, add 2 AP to your AP total. As the repulsorlift's thrusters ignite, you jump away from the vessel before it launches toward the ceiling. The vessel tears a hole through the roof, allowing the smoke to rise out of the factory. You may proceed.

If your new adventure# is less than 7, subtract the difference from your AP total and repeat this confront until you have smashed a hole through the factory's roof. Then you may proceed.

As the smoke clears, you scan the area, looking for any signs of Adi Gallia.

For finding a way to remove the smoke from the interior of the factory, add 200 AP to your AP total. If you've been wearing your breather, you may remove it now.

You notice a computer console just outside the assembly control room. The computer might be wired to a database that lists factory visitors or anyone detained by the security droids. Suddenly, a small box-shaped MSE-6 mouse droid rolls across the floor. Mouse droids don't have weapons and are used to carry information. Placing your foot on top of the skittish mouse droid, you hold it in place while you decide your next move.

To find Adi Gallia, choose to use the Force, interrogate the mouse droid, or access the factory computer. If you have already used Power three times in this adventure, you cannot use Power now.

To use the Force to find Adi Gallia (using Power)*: You must be a Jedi in order to do this. Roll the 20-dice to use the Force to sense your fellow Jedi's whereabouts. Your roll# + your Power# + 3 is your adventure#.

If your adventure# is equal to or more than 11, add the difference to your AP total. In your mind, you sense that Adi Gallia is trapped in the starship factory's observation tower. You may proceed.

If your adventure# is less than 11, subtract the difference from your AP total. You're nervous and distracted. To use Power, you must remain calm. Roll the 20-dice again to relax your mind and become open to the Force. If calm is one of your talents, your new roll# + your knowledge# + your Power# + 2 is your adventure#. If calm is not one of your talents, your new roll# + your Power# + your knowledge# is your new adventure#.

If your new adventure# is equal to or more than 13, add the difference to your AP total. You receive a vision of Adi Gallia trapped within the starship factory's observation tower. You may proceed.

If your new adventure# is less than 13, subtract the difference from your AP total. You are unable to find Adi Gallia by using the Force. Proceed to interrogate the mouse droid or access the factory computer (below).

*NOTE: This counts as one of three Power uses you are allowed on this adventure.

To interrogate the mouse droid:
Roll the 10-dice to search the droid's information storage unit. Your roll# + your skill# is your adventure#.

If your adventure# is equal to or more than 6, add the difference to your AP total. The mouse droid yields the exact information you

54

wanted! Adi Gallia is trapped within the starship factory's observation tower. You may proceed.

If your adventure# is less than 6, subtract 4 AP from your AP total. The only thing inside the mouse droid are Boll Trinkatta's used handkerchiefs. Proceed to access the factory computer (below).

To access the factory computer: Roll the 10-dice to search the factory's database for any mention of Adi Gallia. Your roll# + your knowledge# + 1 is your adventure#.

If your adventure# is equal to or more than 7, add the difference to your AP total. The computer notes a building inspector matching Adi Gallia's description was taken to the starship factory's observation tower. You may proceed.

If your adventure# is less than 7, subtract the difference from your AP total and repeat this confrontation until you have found the information about Adi Gallia. Then you may proceed.

The factory's observation tower is on the other side of the spaceport, which lies just outside the assembly room. Twenty stories tall, the tower appears to be a new structure built on top of an ancient stone foundation. The first seventeen stories rise from the ground as a four-sided obelisk that support an inverted dome — lined with transparisteel windows — that house the three-story observation levels. Five plastoid landing decks jut out from the inverted dome, adding to the tower's crude resemblance to a gigantic, machinelike flower.

Exiting the assembly room, you step out onto the tarmac. Several factory-owned repulsorlift vehicles are parked on the black floor of the spaceport landing area.

A nearby transport vehicle is up on blocks for repair. Under the transport, three old astromech droids turn their cylindrical heads and sight you with their photoreceptors. Brandishing beamdrills and welding tools, the battered astromechs emit a flurry of threatening beeps as they roll toward you. You can't let them stop you from reaching the observation tower.

Choose to evade or combat the astromechs. If you choose to combat, choose to use Power or your lightsaber. If you have already used Power three times in this adventure, you cannot use it now.

To evade the astromechs: Roll the 10-dice to run up the steps of a nearby loading platform. Your roll# + your stealth# is your adventure#.

If your adventure# is equal to or more than 6, add the difference to your AP total. It isn't easy for astromechs to climb steps. As the three droids slowly pivot their way up to the loading platform, you leap down to the tarmac. The excited droids try to follow you, but they tumble down the stairs and roll helplessly on their sides. You may proceed.

If your adventure# is less than 6, subtract the difference from your AP total. As you run up the stairs, the three droids stop in their tracks. Positioned beneath the repulsorlift transport, each droid raises a laser tool at you and prepares to fire. Roll the 20-dice to leap down the stairs. Your new roll# + your stealth# + your strength# is your new adventure#.

If your new adventure# is equal to or more than 13, add the difference to your AP total. You dive away from the droids and they lose sight of you. You may proceed.

If your new adventure# is less than 13, subtract the difference from your AP total. You land on the tarmac and the droids turn fast, directing their laser tools at you. The droids are still positioned under the transport. Proceed to combat the renegade astromechs with your lightsaber (below).

To combat the astromechs with your lightsaber: Roll the 20-dice to use your lightsaber to cut down one of the supporting blocks under the transport. Your roll# + your weaponry# + your lightsaber's mid-range# is your adventure#.

If your adventure# is equal to or more than 13, add the difference to your AP total. Its main supporting block ruined, the transport crashes down upon the three astromechs, crushing them before they can fire their laser tools at you. You may proceed.

If your adventure# is less than 13, subtract the difference from your AP total. Your lightsaber cuts through the supporting block but the transport balances on the remaining blocks. A well placed kick to the side of the transport should bring it crashing to the tarmac. Roll the 10-dice. Your new roll# + your strength# + 1 is your new adventure#.

If your new adventure# is equal to or more than 7, add 2 AP to your AP total. Connecting with the transport, your swift kick topples the repulsorlift onto the rebellious astromechs. You may proceed.

If your new adventure# is less than 7, subtract the difference from your AP total and repeat the confrontation from the line "Roll the 10-dice" until you have kicked the unbalanced transport and knocked it over, crushing the three droids. Then you may proceed.

To combat the astromechs (using Power): Choose your Alteration Power. Roll the 20-dice to make the droids turn their beamdrills on each other. Your roll# + your Power# + your Power's mid-resist# is your adventure#.

If your adventure# is equal to or more than 11, add the difference to your AP total. Using Power to redirect the three droids' beamdrills, you watch as the astromechs activate their dangerous tools. The droids fry each other and you may proceed.

If your adventure# is less than 11, subtract the difference from your AP total and repeat this confrontation from the line *To combat the as-*

tromechs (using Power) until you have used Power to make the three droids destroy each other. Then you may proceed.

*NOTE: This counts as one of three Power uses you are allowed on this adventure.

Surveying the tower's twenty stories, you notice a vehicle resting on the tower's uppermost plastoid deck. The vehicle hadn't been there when you arrived at the factory. It is a bizarre two-seat skyhopper, a fast repulsorlift vehicle designed to fly above the ground. You don't recognize the model. Remembering that Trinkatta's central droid control room is on Level 19 of the tower, it occurs to you that the parked skyhopper might belong to saboteurs, villains intent on taking over Trinkatta's factory by reprogramming his droids. The only way to find out is to go to the tower.

If you can gain access to the control room, you might be able to find out the exact location of Adi Gallia. You can also try deactivating the reprogrammed droids.

It won't take long for you to run to the tower but you'll get there faster if you take a repulsorlift vehicle. To reach the starship factory's observation tower, choose to take a repulsorlift vehicle or run (if flight is one of your talents, you can fly to the tower).

To take a repulsorlift vehicle: Choose your vehicle. It must be capable of flying over land. You strap into the vehicle's safety harness. Roll the 10-dice to speed across the spaceport to the observation tower. Your roll# + your navigation# + your vehicle's speed# is your adventure#.

If your adventure# is equal to or more than 8, add the difference to your AP total. Your selected repulsorlift vehicle zooms over the tarmac, carrying you toward the base of the observation tower. As you near the tower, you try to slow down . . . and discover that the inertial dampers don't work! Proceed to activate the emergency inertial dampers or leap from the vehicle (next page).

If your adventure# is less than 8, subtract 4 AP from your AP total. The repulsorlift vehicle was scheduled for repairs by the three astromechs. You are unable to start the vehicle, and must proceed to run (or fly) to the observation tower (next page).

To activate the emergency inertial dampers: Roll the 10-dice to pull the emergency lever. Your roll# + your strength# + 1 is your adventure#.

If your adventure# is equal to or more than 7, add the difference to your AP total. The vehicle comes to a screeching stop mere centimeters from the tower's foundation. You may proceed.

If your adventure# is less than 7, subtract 5 AP from your AP total. The emergency lever breaks off in your hand. You pulled it too hard! Proceed to leap from the vehicle (below).

To leap from the vehicle: Roll the 20-dice, unbuckle your safety harness, and jump out of the runaway repulsorlift. Your roll# + your stealth# + 2 is your adventure#.

If your adventure# is equal to or more than 13, add the difference to your AP total. You leap from the repulsorlift and roll across the tarmac. The out-of-control vehicle crashes into the tower's foundation. Fortunately, the foundation is not badly damaged and the tower is unaffected. You may proceed.

If your adventure# is less than 13, subtract 9 AP from your AP total. You are unable to unbuckle your safety harness before the vehicle crashes into the wall. The repulsorlift is ruined. At least the safety harness worked. If you hadn't been wearing it, you could have been killed. You may proceed.

To run (or fly) to the observation tower: Roll the 10-dice to cross the distance from the starship factory to the observation tower. If flight is one of your talents, your roll# + your skill# + 1 is your adventure#. If flight is not one of your talents, your roll# + your strength# is your adventure#.

If your adventure# is equal to or more than 7, add the difference to your AP total. Racing over the spaceport tarmac, you reach the observation tower. You may proceed.

If your adventure# is less than 7, subtract the difference from your AP total and repeat until you have arrived at the starship factory's spaceport observation tower. Then you may proceed.

At the base of the observation tower, a door leads to a lift tube. You enter the lift tube and address the lift computer, stating your destination: "Level 19, central droid control."

The lift rises in a powerful rush from ground level. Seconds later, the repulsor field warning light flashes red and the lift screeches to a halt. You are launched off your feet, smashing into the ceiling's emergency escape hatch before crashing back to the floor.

Rising from the floor, you check the lift tube console. According to the numerical display, you are trapped between Levels 18 and 19, just shy of your destination. If the droids tapped into the lift tube computer terminal, your destination command may have alerted them to your position.

Realizing you must get out of the lift tube, you open the emergency escape hatch in the ceiling. Climbing up and through the hatch, you step onto the top of the lift.

Looking upward into the cylindrical tube shaft, you see the sealed doors for Level 19. Suddenly, a whirring motor sounds from above. A shaft maintenance droid, clinging to the walls by its magnetic treads, rapidly descends from the upper levels of the lift tube. Aiming a disrupter at you, the droid prepares to fire.

Using your lightsaber, choose to cut open the doors or combat the shaft maintenance droid.

To cut open the doors: Roll the 20-dice to use your lightsaber to escape through the sealed doors to Level 19. Your roll# + your weaponry# + your weapon's close-range# is your adventure#.

If your adventure# is equal to or more than 13, add the difference to your AP total. Quickly using your lightsaber to cut a hole through the doors to Level 19, you jump through the hole and out of the lift tube. The droid falls smashing into the lift, causing it to plunge through the shaft and crash at the bottom. Safely within Level 19, you may proceed.

If your adventure# is less than 13, subtract the difference from your AP total. Although you've cut a hole through the lift tube doors, the droid will reach you before you can enter Level 19. You must proceed to combat the shaft maintenance droid (next page).

To combat the shaft maintenance droid: Roll the 20-dice to hurl your lightsaber at the oncoming droid. If defense is one of your talents, your roll# + your weaponry# + your lightsaber's far-range# + 2 is your adventure#. If defense is not one of your talents, your roll# + your weaponry# + your lightsaber's far-range# is your adventure#.

If your adventure# is equal to or more than 13, add the difference to your AP total. Tossed upward, your lightsaber rotates and cuts the descending droid in half. Each half of the droid falls past your lift and down the length of the tube. As your lightsaber falls, you catch it by the handle. If you have not already done so, you cut a hole through the doors to Level 19. Entering Level 19, you may proceed.

If your adventure# is less than 13, subtract the difference from your AP total. Braking hard to avoid your hurled lightsaber, the shaft maintenance droid draws its body close to the wall and dodges your blazing weapon. You catch the lightsaber just as the droid comes closer and prepares for another attack. Roll the 20-dice again. If defense is one of your talents, your new roll# + your weaponry# + your lightsaber's close-range# + 1 is your adventure#. If defense is not one of your talents, your new roll# + your weaponry# + your lightsaber's close-range# is your new adventure#.

If your new adventure# is equal to or more than 15, add the difference to your AP total. Swinging furiously, you cut the shaft maintenance droid at its magnetic tread joints, sending its body clattering down the lift tube. If you have not already done so, you cut a hole through the doors to Level 19. Entering Level 19, you may proceed.

If your new adventure# is less than 15, subtract the difference from your AP total and repeat from the line "Roll the 20-dice again" until you have destroyed the droid and cut your way through the doors to Level 19. Then you may proceed.

The lift tube is now damaged and you'll have to find another way out of the observation tower.

For reaching Level 19, add 75 AP to your AP total.

Level 19 is filled with sophisticated computers but appears devoid of droids. Entering the central droid control room, you pass a window that offers a view of the starship factory at the other side of the spaceport. Across the tarmac, droids pour out of the factory and advance toward the observation tower.

Realizing every droid at Trinkatta Starships must be coming after you, you turn your attention to the interior of the control room. While searching for the main terminal that regulates all of the factory's droids, you step into the detention center.

The detention center is a long corridor that ends in a large black metal wall. Five cells line the right wall and another five cells are built into the left. Instead of having sealed metal doors, each cell is viewable through a transparent energy field. From where you are standing, you can't see directly inside any of the cells. You move cautiously forward to inspect them.

Much to your astonishment, you see the same view in each cell: Adi Gallia's motionless form. You realize nine of the cells must contain holographic projections, decoys to delay any rescue attempt. In every cell, Master Adi appears the same. She is slumped on a metal bed with her multitailed headdress spread out under her. Her eyes are closed. She is wearing a heavy brown robe and you can't tell if she's breathing. You yell her name, trying to wake her. But it's no use. You must determine which cell contains the real Adi Gallia and deactivate the energy shields.

A command console is located within the middle of the detention center. There are ten unmarked switches on the command console. The switches might help you free Adi Gallia.

To throw a switch: Roll the 10-dice.

If you roll 1 or 2, you activate a security switch that jolts you with an electric shock. Deduct 3 AP from your AP total and roll again.

If you roll 3 or 4, you deactivate the Adi Gallia holograms. The holograms vanish and the real Adi Gallia remains visible. You must deactivate the energy shields in order to reach her. Roll again to deactivate the shields.

If you roll 5 or 6, the switch opens the black metal wall at the end of the corridor and releases a guard droid. Although humanoid in design, the droid's skeletal arms end with double-barreled blaster rifles. Sighting you, the droid's eyes glow red. You must combat the droid with your lightsaber. Roll the 20-dice to fight the guard droid. If defense is one of your talents, your roll# + your stealth# + your weaponry# + your weapon's close-range# is your adventure#. If defense is not one of your talents, your roll# + your weaponry# + your weapon's close-range# is your adventure#.

If your adventure# is equal to or more than 14, add the difference to your AP total. Your lightsaber flashes and slices the droid in half. The ruined droid crashes to the floor. Roll the 10-dice to throw another switch. **NOTE:** If you roll 5 or 6 again, you have already defeated the guard droid and you may roll again.

If your adventure# is less than 14, subtract the difference from your AP total and repeat from the line "Roll the 20-dice to fight the guard droid" until you have cut down the guard droid. After you have defeated the droid, roll the 10-dice again to throw another switch. **NOTE:** If you roll 5 or 6 again, another guard droid will be released into the detention center, and you will have to fight it before you can proceed.

If you roll 7 or 8, you deactivate both the holograms and the energy shields. Adi Gallia remains visible and you free her from the cell.

If you roll 9 or 10, a panel slides back from the floor, revealing a stairway that leads below the detention level to a secret maintenance room. It is possible this lower chamber will offer clues to help free Master Adi. You approach the stairs. Roll the 10-dice to explore the lower chamber. If tracking is one of your talents, your roll# + your knowledge# + your stealth# + 1 is your adventure#. If tracking is not one of your talents, your roll# + your stealth# is your adventure#.

If your adventure# is equal to or more than 8, add the difference to your AP total. The secret chamber contains a hydraulic lift beneath each cell. You find some oddly-shaped footprints on the floor near one of the lifts. The footprints appear to have been made by a large insectoid creature, possibly while placing Adi Gallia on the lift that raised her to an upper cell. If that's true, then Master Adi is within the cell directly above you. Proceed to lower the lift (below).

If your adventure# is less than 8, subtract the difference from your AP total. As you approach the stairs, the floor panel suddenly slides shut, preventing you from exploring the lower level. You return your attention to the ten switches on the console. Roll the 10-dice again to throw another switch.

To lower the lift: Roll the 10-dice to pull a level that will make the upper cell descend into the secret chamber. Your roll# + your skill# + 2 is your adventure#.

If your adventure# is equal to or more than 8, add the difference to your AP total. The hydraulic lift sinks into the floor, lowering the cell from above. The cell contains Adi Gallia!

If your adventure# is less than 8, subtract the difference from your AP total. You pulled the wrong lever. Go back to the line *To lower the lift* and try again.

You enter Adi Gallia's cell and run to her side. You bend down and check her vital signs. She's unconscious and requires medical attention.

For locating Adi Gallia, add 150 AP to your AP total.

You carry Adi Gallia out of the detention center. You have to get her out of the observation tower, but first you must deal with the incoming droids. If you can transmit a signal from the central droid control room, you might be able to reprogram the droids. A quicker solution would be to destroy the control tower; this would make all the droids stop functioning, but it could also get you killed if you don't escape the tower in time.

Finding the main terminal, choose to reprogram the factory droids or destroy the control room.

To reprogram the factory droids: Roll the 20-dice to enter new commands into the control terminal. Your roll# + your knowledge# + 2 is your adventure#.

If your adventure# is equal to or more than 14, add the difference to your AP total. Entering the new commands, you manage to broadcast a signal from the control room. The signal makes all the factory droids surrender their weapons and freeze in their tracks. You have successfully reprogrammed the droids, but sparks begin to fly from the control terminal.

A yellow warning light flashes and an alarm begins to ring. By tampering with the controls, you have triggered an emergency security system that will blow up the tower. You have less than three minutes to escape the tower with Adi Gallia. You may proceed.

If your adventure# is less than 14, subtract the difference from your AP total. You enter the wrong command, and accidentally make the droids run faster for the observation tower. Unless you can reprogram the droids, they'll reach the tower in seconds. Roll the 20-dice again. Your new roll# + your knowledge# + 1 is your new adventure#.

> *If your new adventure# is equal to or more than 12,* add 2 AP to your AP total. Entering the new commands, you reprogram the droids to surrender. But sparks begin to fly from the control terminal. A yellow warning light flashes and an alarm begins to ring. By tampering with the controls, you have triggered an emergency security system that will blow up the tower. You have less than three minutes to escape the tower with Adi Gallia. You may proceed.

> *If your new adventure# is less than 12,* subtract the difference from your AP total. Failing to enter the correct commands, you

must proceed to destroy the control room (below).

To destroy the control room: Roll the 20-dice to enter an auto-destruct command in the main terminal of central droid control. Your roll# + your knowledge# + your skill# is your adventure#.

If your adventure# is equal to or more than 13, add the difference to your AP total. Having entered the auto-destruct command into the computer, you now have three minutes to escape the tower with Adi Gallia. You may proceed.

If your adventure# is less than 13, subtract the difference from your AP total and repeat this confront until you have set the central droid control room for auto-destruct. The tower will explode in three minutes. You may proceed.

If the droids were not reprogrammed to surrender, the imminent destruction of central droid control will cause them to stop functioning.

Since the lift tube is ruined, you must find another way out of the observation tower. Remembering the bizarre skyhopper on the tower's upper deck, you pick up Adi Gallia from the floor and carry her up the emergency stairway. You will use the skyhopper to escape the tower.

Exiting the stairwell, you notice the egress door has been kicked in from the outside. As you proceed through the damaged doorway, you wonder what has become of the saboteurs.

When you reach the upper deck, you find the skyhopper parked in the same spot. Without warning, two tall insectoid aliens step out from behind the skyhopper. With their black body armor and segmented movements, you recognize the aliens at once.

They're Bartokks.

A race of bloodthirsty mercenaries, the Bartokks are notorious throughout the galaxy for their assassin squads. With their hive mind, they work together to kill their assigned targets. Each Bartokk stands on two powerful legs and has four arms: two manipulatory arms extend from their waists while their upper arms end in long hooked claws.

Although you don't know the Bartokks' motives for invading the factory, you gather that they are responsible for reprogramming the starship factory droids and subduing Adi Gallia. Before you can question them, the two insectoid aliens raise their claws and advance.

Placing Adi Gallia on the floor of the deck, you brace yourself for the Bartokks' attack. Jedi do not believe in killing unless it is absolutely necessary, but Bartokks are professional killers who won't hesitate to slice you from head to toe.

Choose to dodge or combat the Bartokks.

To dodge the Bartokks: Roll the 10-dice to dodge the oncoming Bartokks. If defense is one of your talents, your roll# + your stealth# + 2 is your adventure#. If defense is not one of your talents, your roll# + your stealth# is your adventure#.

If your adventure# is equal to or more than 7, add the difference to your AP total. Dodging the two Bartokks, you miss being skewered by their claws. Running past you, the Bartokks fall off the edge of the high tower, plummeting to their doom. You may proceed.

If your adventure# is less than 7, subtract the difference from your AP total. The Bartokks are sure-footed aliens and you can't dodge them. They will not walk away from this fight unless they kill you. Proceed to combat the Bartokks by using your lightsaber (below) or Power (next page).

To combat the Bartokks using your lightsaber: Roll the 20-dice to cut down the Bartokks. Your roll# + your weaponry# + your lightsaber's mid-range# + 1 is your adventure#.

If your adventure# is equal to or more than 15, add the difference to your AP total. Leaving you without any possibility for a peaceful solution, the Bartokks are victim to your quick skill with a lightsaber. You may proceed.

If your adventure# is less than 15, subtract the difference from your AP total. You only wounded the fierce Bartokks and now they're out for your blood. Roll the 10-dice again. Your new roll# + your weaponry# + your lightsaber's close-range# + 1 is your new adventure#.

If your new adventure# is equal to or more than 13, add 2 AP to your AP total. Defeating the two Bartokks, you may proceed.

If your new adventure# is less than 13, subtract the difference from your AP total and repeat from the line "Roll the 10-dice again" until you have killed the ferocious Bartokks. Then you may proceed.

Racing to Adi Gallia's unconscious form, you pick her up and proceed to escape the tower. If flight is one of your abilities, you can carry Adi Gallia as you spread your wings and fly to the ground. If flight is not one of your abilities, you place Adi Gallia into the Bartokks' skyhopper.

To escape the tower: Roll the 20-dice to fly away with Adi Gallia from the tower. If flight is one of your talents, your roll# + your stealth# + your strength# is your adventure#. If flight is not one of your talents, your roll# + your navigation# + 2 is your adventure#.

If your adventure# is equal to or more than 14, add the difference to your AP total. Soaring away with Adi Gallia from the tower, you may proceed.

If your adventure# is less than 14, subtract the difference from your AP total. A powerful gust of wind tosses you through the air, back toward the tower. You must fly away from the tower before it explodes. Roll the 10-dice to adjust the flight path. If flight is one of your talents, your new roll# + your power# + your strength# + your stealth# is your adventure#. If flight is not one of your talents, your new roll# + your navigation# + your skill# is your new adventure#.

If your new adventure# is equal to or more than 8, add the difference to your AP total. You expertly soar away from the tower, carrying Adi Gallia with you. You may proceed.

If your new adventure# is less than 8, subtract the difference from your AP total. Go back to "Roll the 10-dice to adjust your flight path" and repeat until you and Adi Gallia have flown safely away from the observation tower. Then you may proceed.

The control room explodes. The power of the blast nearly knocks both you and Adi Gallia out of the sky, but you land safely outside the barricade surrounding Trinkatta Starships. Scanning the area, you see the other Jedi running from the factory's security checkpoint. Busy fighting the droids during your adventure, your friends had almost given up on both you and Adi Gallia. Seeing that you and Adi Gallia are both alive, they are joyous.

"It's hardly time to celebrate!" you tell them. "Adi Gallia is unconscious and requires medical treatment! Also, I couldn't find the fifty droid starfighters. But I learned they were ordered by the Trade Federation. Even worse, I had a run-in with Bartokk assassins."

Hearing this information, your friends' joy changes to concern, and they realize your adventure is only just beginning!

For rescuing Adi Gallia and ending the threat of the starship factory droids, add 500 AP to your AP total.

To read the end of this adventure, please turn to page 77 of your Adventure Novel, *Search for the Lost Jedi*!